Year 4 - Independent Writing Activities

Introduction

This book of 'Independent Writing Activities' covers the genres for the 8 to 9 year old age group. It has been written to the UK National Strategy Primary Framework for Literacy.

It contains at least two independent writing activities for each genre type and is an ideal vehicle for assessing pupil progress in writing when used with the different Levels found in the Writing Assessment Guidelines, which accompany the Primary Framework for Literacy. (The appropriate levels for this age group have been reproduced under licence at the beginning of this book.)

The author has also used this approach successfully with children to embed the features of each genre. This was achieved by re-visiting a previously studied genre later in the term, so that the children practised it once again. This ensured that the features of that particular type of writing remained firmly embedded in the children's memory. Thus when the children were tested or came to write in that particular genre at a later date it was not just a distant memory.

There are six similar books in this series covering the work of pupils from Year 1 through to Year 6 (ages 5 to 11). PDF or Download versions are also available of these books for use on Interactive Whiteboards.

Index

Narrative

The Other World
Stimulus	4
Planning notes	5
Final Written Work	6

The Evacuees
Stimulus	7
Planning notes	8
Final Written Work	9

Keep Out of the Mud
Stimulus	10
Planning notes	11
Final Written Work	12

Play Script

The New Family
Stimulus	13
Planning notes	14
Final Written Work	15

The Empty House
Stimulus	16
Planning notes	17
Final Written Work	18

Recount

Healthy Schools Week
Stimulus	19
Planning notes	20
Final Written Work	21

Playtime Activities
Stimulus	22
Planning notes	23
Final Written Work	24

Stimulus	25
Planning notes	26
Final Written Work	27

The Helifish
Stimulus	28
Planning notes	29
Final Written Work	30

Explanation

Push-Along Cart
Stimulus	31
Planning notes	32
Final Written Work	33

How to Look After a Pet
Stimulus	34
Planning notes	35
Final Written Work	36

Persuasion

School Uniform
Stimulus	37
Planning notes	38
Final Written Work	39

Choco Power!
Stimulus	40
Planning notes	41
Final Written Work	42

Poetry

Night / Morning Poem
Stimulus	43
Planning notes	44
Final Written Work	45

Acrostic Poetry
Stimulus	46
Planning notes	47
Final Written Work	48

Topical Resources publishes a range of Educational Materials for use in Primary Schools and Pre-School Nurseries and Playgroups.

Copyright © 2009 Heather Bell
First Published September 2009.
ISBN: 978-1-907269-02-8

Illustrated by John Hutchinson, Art Works, Fairhaven, 69 Worden Lane, Leyland, Preston

Designed by Paul Sealey, PS3 Creative, 3 Wentworth Drive, Thornton, Lancashire.

Printed in the UK for 'Topical Resources' by T. Snape and Co Ltd., Boltons Court, Preston, Lancashire.

For the latest catalogue
Tel 01772 863158
Fax 01772 866153
email: sales@topical-resources.co.uk

Visit our Website at:
www.topical-resources.co.uk

Writing assessment guidelines: levels 2 and 3

Pupil name _____ Class/Group _____ Date _____

	AF5 – vary sentences for clarity, purpose and effect	AF6 – write with technical accuracy of syntax and punctuation in phrases, clauses and sentences	AF3 – organise and present whole texts effectively, sequencing and structuring information, ideas and events	AF4 – construct paragraphs and use cohesion within and between paragraphs	AF1 – write imaginative, interesting and thoughtful texts	AF2 – produce texts which are appropriate to task, reader and purpose	AF7 – select appropriate and effective vocabulary	AF8 – use correct spelling	Handwriting and presentation
Level 3	**In most writing** • reliance mainly on simply structured sentences, variation with support, *e.g. some complex sentences* • *and, but, so* are the most common connectives, subordination occasionally • some limited variation in use of tense and verb forms, not always secure	**In most writing** • straightforward sentences usually demarcated accurately with full stops, capital letters, question and exclamation marks • some, limited, use of speech punctuation • comma splicing evident, particularly in narrative	**In most writing** • some attempt to organise ideas with related points placed next to each other • openings and closings usually signalled • some attempt to sequence ideas or material logically	**In most writing** • some internal structure within sections of text *e.g. one-sentence paragraphs or ideas loosely organised* • within paragraphs/sections, some links between sentences, *e.g. use of pronouns or of adverbials* • movement between paragraphs/sections sometimes abrupt or disjointed	**In most writing** • some appropriate ideas and content included • some attempt to elaborate on basic information or events, *e.g. nouns expanded by simple adjectives* • attempt to adopt viewpoint, though often not maintained or inconsistent, *e.g. attitude expressed, but with little elaboration*	**In most writing** • purpose established at a general level • main features of selected form sometimes signalled to the reader • some attempts at appropriate style, with attention to reader	**In most writing** • simple, generally appropriate vocabulary used, limited in range • some words selected for effect or occasion	**In most writing** • correct spelling of some common grammatical function words common content/lexical words with more than one morpheme, including compound words • likely errors *some inflected endings, e.g. past tense, comparatives, adverbs some phonetically plausible attempts at content/lexical words*	**In most writing** • legible style, shows accurate and consistent letter formation, sometimes joined
Level 2	**In some forms of writing** • some variation in sentence openings, *e.g. not always starting with name or pronoun* • mainly simple sentences with *and* used to connect clauses • past and present tense generally consistent	**In some forms of writing** • clause structure mostly grammatically correct • sentence demarcation with capital letters and full stops usually accurate • some accurate use of question and exclamation marks, and commas in lists	**In some forms of writing** • some basic sequencing of ideas or material, *e.g. time-related words or phrases, line breaks, headings, numbers* • openings and/or closings sometimes signalled	**In some forms of writing** • ideas in sections grouped by content, some linking by simple pronouns	**In some forms of writing** • mostly relevant ideas and content, sometimes repetitive or sparse • some apt word choices create interest • brief comments, questions about events or actions suggest viewpoint	**In some forms of writing** • some basic purpose established, *e.g. main features of story, report* • some appropriate features of the given form used • some attempts to adopt appropriate style	**In some forms of writing** • simple, often speech-like vocabulary conveys relevant meanings • some adventurous word choices, *e.g. opportune use of new vocabulary*	**In some forms of writing** • usually correct spelling of high frequency grammatical function words common single morpheme content/lexical words • likely errors *inflected endings, e.g. past tense, plurals, adverbs phonetic attempts at vowel digraphs*	**In some forms of writing** • letters generally correctly shaped but inconsistencies in orientation, size and use of upper/lower case letters • clear letter formation, with ascenders and descenders distinguished, generally upper and lower case letters not mixed within words
BL									
IE									

Key: BL Below level   IE Insufficient evidence

Overall assessment (tick one box only)

Low 2	Secure 2	High 2	Low 3	Secure 3	High 3
☐	☐	☐	☐	☐	☐

QCA

Writing assessment guidelines: levels 3 and 4

Pupil name _____ Class/Group _____ Date _____

	AF5 – vary sentences for clarity, purpose and effect	AF6 – write with technical accuracy of syntax and punctuation in phrases, clauses and sentences	AF3 – organise and present whole texts effectively, sequencing and structuring information, ideas and events	AF4 – construct paragraphs and use cohesion within and between paragraphs	AF1 – write imaginative, interesting and thoughtful texts	AF2 – produce texts which are appropriate to task, reader and purpose	AF7 – select appropriate and effective vocabulary	AF8 – use correct spelling	Handwriting and presentation
Level 4	**Across a range of writing** • some variety in length, structure or subject of sentences • use of some subordinating connectives, *e.g. if, when, because* throughout the text • some variation, generally accurate, in tense and verb forms	**Across a range of writing** • sentences demarcated accurately throughout the text, including question marks • speech marks to denote speech generally accurate, with some other speech punctuation • commas used in lists and occasionally to mark clauses, although not always accurately	**Across a range of writing** • ideas organised by clustering related points or by time sequence • ideas are organised simply with a fitting opening and closing, sometimes linked • ideas or material generally in logical sequence but overall direction of writing not always clearly signalled	**Across a range of writing** • paragraphs/sections help to organise content, *e.g. main idea usually supported or elaborated by following sentences* • within paragraphs/sections, limited range of connections between sentences, *e.g. over-use of 'also' or pronouns* • some attempts to establish simple links between paragraphs/sections not always maintained, *e.g. firstly, next*	**Across a range of writing** • relevant ideas and content chosen • some ideas and material developed in detail, *e.g. descriptions elaborated by adverbial and expanded noun phrases* • straightforward viewpoint generally established and maintained, *e.g. writing in role or maintaining a consistent stance*	**Across a range of writing** • main purpose of writing is clear but not always consistently maintained • main features of selected form are clear and appropriate to purpose • style generally appropriate to task, though awareness of reader not always sustained	**Across a range of writing** • some evidence of deliberate vocabulary choices • some expansion of general vocabulary to match topic	**Across a range of writing** • correct spelling of most common grammatical function words, including adverbs with -ly formation regularly formed content/lexical words, including those with multiple morphemes • most past and present tense inflections, plurals • likely errors • *homophones of some common grammatical function words* • *occasional phonetically plausible spelling in content/lexical words*	
Level 3	**In most writing** • reliance mainly on simply structured sentences, variation with support, *e.g. some complex sentences* • *and, but, so* are the most common connectives, subordination occasionally • some limited variation in use of tense and verb forms, not always secure	**In most writing** • straightforward sentences usually demarcated accurately with full stops, capital letters, question and exclamation marks • some, limited, use of speech punctuation • comma splicing evident, particularly in narrative	**In most writing** • some attempt to organise ideas with related points placed next to each other • openings and closings usually signalled • some attempt to sequence ideas or material logically	**In most writing** • some internal structure within sections of text *e.g. one-sentence paragraphs or ideas loosely organised* • within paragraphs/sections, some links between sentences, *e.g. use of pronouns or of adverbials* • movement between paragraphs/sections sometimes abrupt or disjointed	**In most writing** • some appropriate ideas and content included • some attempt to elaborate on basic information or events, *e.g. nouns expanded by simple adjectives* • attempt to adopt viewpoint, though often not maintained or inconsistent, *e.g. attitude expressed, but with little elaboration*	**In most writing** • purpose established at a general level • main features of selected form sometimes signalled to the reader • some attempts at appropriate style, with attention to reader	**In most writing** • simple, generally appropriate vocabulary used, limited in range • some words selected for effect or occasion	**In most writing** • correct spelling of some common grammatical function words common content/lexical words with more than one morpheme, including compound words • likely errors • *some inflected endings, e.g. past tense, comparatives, adverbs* • *some phonetically plausible attempts at content/lexical words*	**In most writing** • legible style, shows accurate and consistent letter formation, sometimes joined
BL									
IE									

Key: BL Below level   IE Insufficient evidence

Overall assessment (tick one box only)

☐ Low 3   ☐ Secure 3   ☐ High 3   ☐ Low 4   ☐ Secure 4   ☐ High 4

QCA

© Crown copyright 2008

The Other World

Read the following extract:

Emma and Tom are walking along the cliffs high above the sea when a very strange event takes place.

Emma looked ahead. Tom was there one minute and the next he was gone. She ran to the spot shouting.

"Tom! Stop messing about. Where are you?"

All of a sudden she felt herself falling downwards and with a thud she landed on the damp floor of a cave.

Tom was busy brushing mud and moss from his clothes.

"Where on earth are we?" asked Emma?

"I don't know," answered Tom, "but it sure feels very strange."

They walked to the entrance of the cave and found themselves in a place unlike any they had ever seen before.

Task

Your task is to continue the story describing the place, who they meet and finally how they get back.

Name _____   Date _____

The Other World

The characters in this story are:

What is the place like?

Who do the children meet?

How did they get home?

Useful descriptive words and phrases:

Name _____　　Date _____

The Other World

Emma and Tom are walking along the cliffs high above the sea when a very strange event takes place.

Emma looked ahead. Tom was there one minute and the next he was gone. She ran to the spot shouting.

"Tom! Stop messing about. Where are you?"

All of a sudden she felt herself falling downwards and with a thud she landed on the damp floor of a cave.

Tom was busy brushing mud and moss from his clothes.

"Where on earth are we?" asked Emma?

"I don't know," answered Tom, "but it sure feels very strange."

They walked to the entrance of the cave and found themselves in a place unlike any they had ever seen before.

_____

_____

_____

_____

_____

_____

_____

_____

_____

_____

_____

_____

The Evacuees

During the Second World War children were evacuated. This means they were taken out of the cities to go and live in the country to keep them safe from aircraft bombing raids.

The children's parents did not go with them - they went alone.

Read the following extract in which two children from London arrive in the small country village of Suddum.

The train pulled to a halt. Mary and John were led with the other children from the station to the village hall. A number of local villagers and farmers had gathered to choose who they would look after. A large burly farmer and his wife who had a smiley face beamed down at Mary and John.

" You two are to come with us to stay at Greengate Farm," said the farmer.

The two children, weary from their long journey, looking small and lost, picked up their bags and followed the couple outside.

Task

Your task is to write the story which follows this passage. You need to write about the new life the children experience on the farm, the family they are staying with and their eventual return home.

Name _____ Date _____

The Evacuees

Where is the story set? What was the farm/village like?

↓

Characters: What were the children like? What was the family they stayed with like?

↓

How did the children feel when they arrived? What did the family feel about the children?

↓

What tasks are the children given on the farm? How is it different from their normal home in the city?

↓

How long are the children evacuated for? How do they feel when they have to return home?

Name _____   **Date** _____

The Evacuees

_____

_____

_____

_____

_____

_____

_____

_____

_____

_____

_____

_____

_____

_____

_____

_____

_____

_____

_____

_____

_____

_____

_____

_____

Keep Out of the Mud

George has a little brother who is just four years old. His mother needed to visit his grandma who was sick. She asked George to look after Alfie for the afternoon. However, George had planned to build a den with his friends in Bluebell Wood.

His mother's last words to George were, "Whatever you do, don't let Alfie get dirty. He is to go to a birthday party at four o'clock and I won't have time to get him changed."

Task

Your task is to write a story with the title 'Keep Out of the Mud'. It tells how George tries to join his friends to help build the den and look after Alfie at the same time – possibly with a disastrous result!

Name _____   Date _____

Keep Out of the Mud

Story Setting: Where is the den to be built?.

Characters:

George:_____

Alfie: _____

Friend 1: _____

Friend 2: _____

The story begins when George is left alone with Alfie. What do they decide to do?

What happens to Alfie when the boys are building a den? Why?

What does George do to resolve the problem?

What happens when his mother comes home?

Name _____   Date _____

Keep Out of the Mud

_____

_____

_____

_____

_____

_____

_____

_____

_____

_____

_____

_____

_____

_____

_____

_____

_____

_____

_____

_____

_____

_____

_____

_____

The New Family

A new family has moved in next door to Suraj. The new boy, Dominic, is of a similar age to Suraj. The two boys see each other for the first time when they meet in the gardens behind their houses. They have the following conversation over the fence...

Suraj: (Shyly leaning on the fence) Have you just moved in?

Dominic: (Pleased to have someone to talk to) Yes. My name is Dominic. What's your name?

Suraj: My name's Suraj. Do you like football?

Task

Your task is to write a play script continuing the conversation between the two boys in which they talk about things they enjoy doing, their feelings and school.

Name _____   **Date** _____

The New Family

Think about the characters in the play. What are they like?

Suraj: _____

Dominic: _____

What does each boy like doing? Do they like the same things or do they like different things?

Who does each boy live with? Do the boys have any family of similar ages? If so, what are they like?

© **Topical Resources.** May be photocopied for classroom use only.

Name _____   **Date** _____

The New Family

Suraj: (Shyly leaning on the fence) Have you just moved in?

Dominic: (Pleased to have someone to talk to) Yes. My name is Dominic. What's your name?

Suraj: My name's Suraj. Do you like football?

_____

_____

_____

_____

_____

_____

_____

_____

_____

_____

_____

_____

_____

_____

_____

_____

_____

_____

_____

The Empty House

Two friends decide to go and explore an empty house. The beginning of the conversation is in the box below...

Billy: (Nervously) Do you think we dare go inside?

Cara: (Looking excited and brave) Oh come on, let's go in. I'm sure it's empty.

Billy: What do you think we will find?

Cara: You never know, there might be treasure!

Task

Your task is to write a play script continuing the conversation between the friends as they explore the house but discover it is not as empty as they thought!

Name _____   **Date** _____

The Empty House

Think about the characters in the play. What are they like?

Billy: _____

Cara: _____

What do they see inside the house?

Why is the house not as empty as they thought?

Name _____   **Date** _____

The Empty House

Billy: (Nervously) Do you think we dare go inside?

Cara: (Looking excited and brave) Oh come on, let's go in. I'm sure it's empty.

Billy: What do you think we will find?

Cara: You never know, there might be treasure!

_____

_____

_____

_____

_____

_____

_____

_____

_____

_____

_____

_____

_____

_____

_____

Healthy Schools Week

Read the box below. Here are some of the activities and events that took place at Green Street School during the 'Healthy Schools Week'.

keep fit

Fun run

exer cise to m usic

healthy eating

Task

Your task is to write a magazine article reporting on the events that took place at Green Street School during Healthy Schools Week. You will need to include some events you have made up yourself.

Name _____   Date _____

Healthy Schools Week

Snappy title:

Other events that may have taken place during Healthy Schools Week:

Useful words and phrases for your magazine report:

Name _____　**Date** _____

Healthy Schools Week

_____
_____
_____
_____
_____
_____
_____
_____
_____
_____
_____
_____
_____
_____
_____
_____
_____
_____
_____
_____
_____
_____
_____
_____
_____

Playtime Activities

The Parents and Friends Association at your school have given a large amount of money to be spent on playground activities and equipment.

Task

Your task is to write a report for the school newsletter explaining what the money has been used for and how the children feel about it.

Name _____   **Date** _____

Playtime Activities

Snappy title:

Items bought for children to play with on the playground at break time:

Items bought for children to play with during a wet playtime:

How the children feel about the new activities:

Name _____   **Date** _____

Playtime Activities

_____

_____

_____

_____

_____

_____

_____

_____

_____

_____

_____

_____

_____

_____

_____

_____

_____

_____

_____

_____

_____

_____

_____

_____

_____

_____

How Seeds are Scattered

Look at the diagrams below, which explain the different ways in which seeds are scattered.

Some seeds are scattered by the wind.

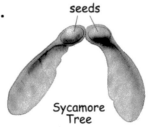
seeds

Sycamore Tree

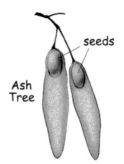
seeds

Ash Tree

On some trees the fruits have 'wings'.

Some seeds are scattered by animals.

Some seeds stick to animal fur.

Birds eat fruit and drop the seeds.

Some seeds are scattered by water.

Squirrels bury nuts.

Some seeds are scattered by exploding fruit such as peas or beans.

Task

Your task is to write an information sheet to explain the different ways seeds are scattered.

Name _____　　Date _____

How Seeds are Scattered

Title:

↓

Introduction:

↓

Seeds scattered by the wind:

↓

Seeds scattered by animals:

↓

Seeds scattered by explosion:

↓

Seeds scattered by water:

Name _____ **Date** _____

How Seeds are Scattered

_____

_____

_____

_____

_____

_____

_____

_____

_____

_____

_____

_____

_____

_____

_____

_____

_____

_____

_____

_____

_____

_____

_____

_____

_____

The Helifish

Here is a picture of the newly discovered Helifish.

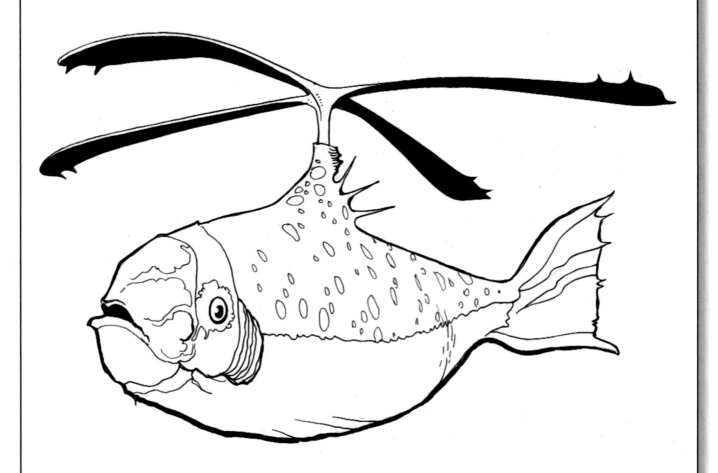

Task

Your task is to write an information sheet for a website which explains the following: How the Helifish was discovered, what the creature looks like, where it is found, what it eats, how it moves and is it dangerous to humans?

Name _____   Date _____

The Helifish

Title:

↓

Introduction/how it was discovered:

↓

What it looks like:

↓

Where it is found/what it eats:

↓

How it moves:

↓

Is it dangerous to humans and if so, how?

Name _____   Date _____

The Helifish

_____
_____
_____
_____
_____
_____
_____
_____
_____
_____
_____
_____
_____
_____
_____
_____
_____
_____
_____
_____
_____
_____
_____
_____
_____
_____

Push-Along Cart

Here is a picture of a push-along cart with wooden bricks inside. Young children often use these when they are learning to walk.

Task

Your task is to write an information leaflet which explains what it is and how it works. Remember to include a simple labelled diagram.

Name _____   **Date** _____

Push-Along Cart

Title:

↓

Introduction explaining what the toy does and who would use it:

↓

How the toy works and what it is made of:

↓

Uses for the toy:

↓

Labels for your diagram:

Name _____ Date _____

Push-Along Cart

_____

_____

_____

_____

_____

_____

_____

_____

_____

_____

_____

_____

_____

_____

_____

_____

_____

_____

_____

_____

_____

_____

_____

How to Look After a Pet

Here is a picture of a pet dog with information about how to look after it.

Feed dog meal and meat.

Always have water available.

Take for regular walks.

West Highland Terrier.

Have hair cut every three months.

Train it as a puppy.

Task

Your task is to write an information leaflet on how to look after a pet of your choice. Remember to include where it sleeps, what and how often it should be fed, exercise required and how to keep it healthy.

Name _____   Date _____

How to Look After a Pet

Title:

⬇

Introduction:

⬇

Where it sleeps/lives:

⬇

What and how often it should be fed:

⬇

Exercise/keeping it healthy:

Name _____ Date _____

How to Look After a Pet

School Uniform

Here is a piece of persuasive writing suggesting the point of view that school uniform is very important.

It is vital that we keep school uniform and maintain a tradition that has been in existence for years. It is traditions like these which make the British Educational system the envy of the world!

School uniform brings discipline, encourages good behaviour and sets standards which will ensure pupils give of their best. The garments are simple, easily replaced and kept clean.

They prevent 'Mr Rich's' son from becoming the hero just because he has the right designer label.

School uniform is a way of giving everyone the same chance, the same opportunity, of making everyone equal.

Whatever happens school uniform must stay!

Task

Your task is to create a piece of persuasive writing that argues against having school uniform. Make your leaflet as persuasive as possible.

Name _____   Date _____

School Uniform

Reasons for
not
having a school uniform

Persuasive words and phrases:

Name _____   Date _____

School Uniform

_____
_____
_____
_____
_____
_____
_____
_____
_____
_____
_____
_____
_____
_____
_____
_____
_____
_____
_____
_____
_____
_____
_____
_____
_____
_____
_____
_____

Choco Power!

Here is a picture of a new chocolate bar.

Task

Your task is to design an advertising poster to persuade as many people as possible to buy a bar of 'Choco Power!' Think about the ingredients, how healthy it is, the cost, the taste and where you can buy it.

Name _____   Date _____

Choco Power!

Ingredients

Healthy?

Main features of 'Choco Power!'

The cost and where you can buy it

Taste words

Imaginative and persuasive words:

Name _____   Date _____

Choco Power!

_____

_____

_____

_____

_____

_____

_____

_____

_____

_____

_____

_____

_____

_____

_____

_____

_____

_____

_____

_____

_____

_____

Choco Power!

Read the poem below:

Night
Cats howling
Car doors banging
Babies wailing
Wind whistling
Curtains flapping
Grandma snoring
Footsteps tapping
Voices whispering
People laughing
Owls hooting
Stairs creaking
Dogs barking
Clocks chiming
Night

Night Poem

Task

Your task is to write a poem similar in style and content with the title 'Morning'.

Name _____   Date _____

Morning Poem

Sounds

Sights

Morning

Tastes

Events

Descriptive words and phrases:

Name _____ **Date** _____

Morning Poem

_____

_____

_____

_____

_____

_____

_____

_____

_____

_____

_____

_____

_____

_____

_____

_____

_____

_____

_____

_____

_____

_____

_____

_____

Acrostic Poetry

Read the Acrostic poem below. The poem is about a junk shop. The title can be seen in the capital letters at the beginning of each line of the poem.

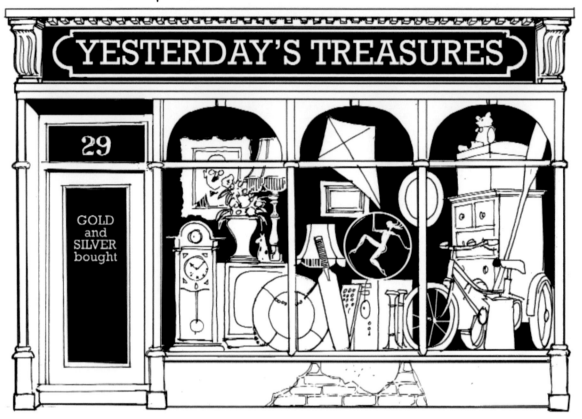

Jewels and gems gleam in bright coloured brooches
Useless broken chairs carelessly piled on grubby rugs
Nothing new, everything old
Knick-knacks, bric a brac from dusty attics

Statues of music composers and chipped garden gnomes
Hairy teddies slightly bald from years of cuddles
Old cups and saucers chipped and cracked
People rummaging, looking for bargains

Task

Your task is to write a poem using one of the following acrostics:
- BIRTHDAY
- CHRISTMAS
- SATURDAY

Name _____ Date _____

Acrostic Poetry

Your Title: Collect descriptive words and phrases

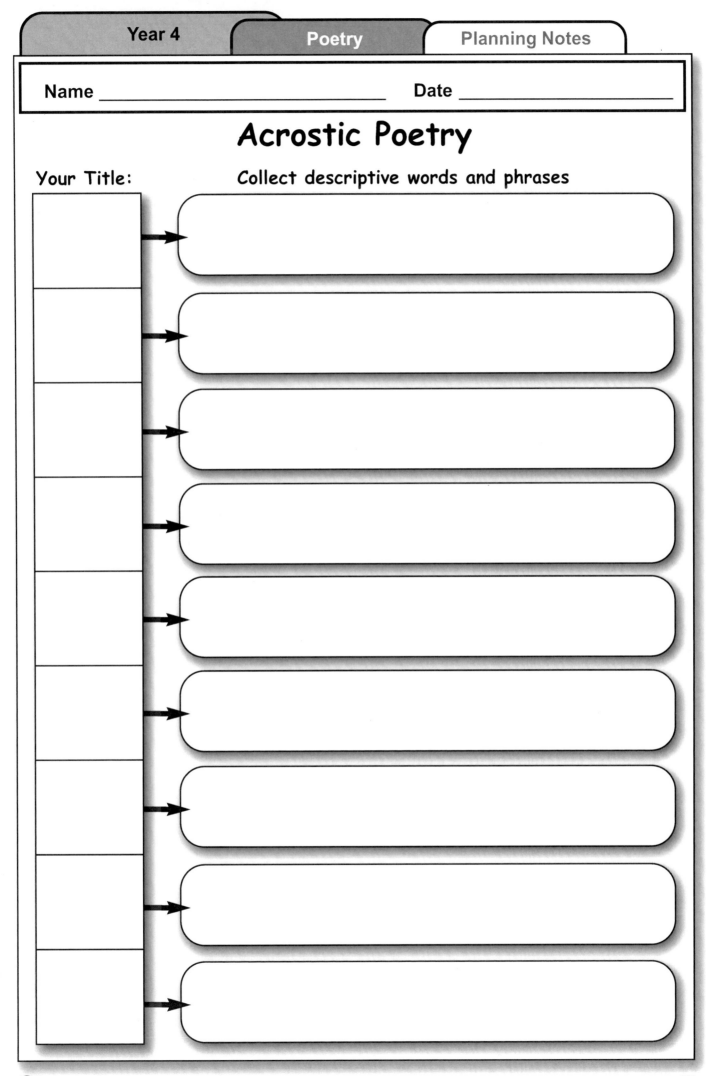

Name _____   Date _____

Acrostic Poetry

_____

_____

_____

_____

_____

_____

_____

_____

_____

_____

_____

_____

_____

_____

_____

_____

_____

_____

_____

_____

_____